The Higgledy Piggledy Pigs

Mummy Pig

Posy Pig

Granny Pig

Daddy Pig

Pip Pig

Baby Pig

To my higgledy-piggledy
family: Daisy, Milo and Tom – SC

For the dear Alice – BN

First published 2004 by Macmillan Children's Books
This edition published 2005 by Macmillan Children's Books
a division of Macmillan Publishers Limited
20 New Wharf Road, London N1 9RR
Basingstoke and Oxford
Associated companies throughout the world
www.panmacmillan.com

ISBN: 978-1-4050-2063-3

Text copyright © Sally Crabtree 2004
Illustrations copyright © Barbara Nascimbeni 2004
Moral rights asserted.

3 5 7 9 8 6 4

A CIP catalogue record for this book is available from the British Library.

Printed in China

SALLY CRABTREE

The Higgledy Piggledy Pigs

Illustrated by Barbara Nascimbeni

MACMILLAN CHILDREN'S BOOKS

At the end of a higgledy-piggledy lane,
in a higgledy-piggledy house,
lived the Higgledy Piggledy Pigs –

Mummy, Daddy and Granny Pig,

Pip, Posy and Baby Pig.

As you can see, they
lived in rather a muddle.

"Rather a muddle!"
exclaimed Mummy Pig.
"This isn't a muddle!
It's a pigsty! And it's
time we did something
about it."

"But we like it like this," said Pip.
"It's cosy," said Gran.
"It's home," said Posy.

"It's a mess,"
said Mum,
"and we're going
to tidy it up!"

It took them all day . . .

Pip tidied
the bathroom.

Posy tidied
the playroom.

Gran tidied
the kitchen.

And Mum tidied
the sitting room.

Baby Pig, who was too little
to tidy, just sat and played.

When they'd finished, the Higgledy Piggledy Pigs looked around.

"Isn't it wonderful?" said Mum.
"It feels cold," said Gran.
"It's a bit empty," said Posy.
"Yes," said Pip glumly.

Suddenly, Baby Pig
began to cry.

"Waa!"

"See – he doesn't
Like it, either," Said Pip.

"NO," said Posy.
"NO," said Gran.
"Waa!" said Baby Pig.

"It can't be the tidy room," said Mum.
"Whatever's the matter?"
Then she realized.
"It's his teddy. He's lost it!"

"Oh dear, we must have tidied it up!"
shouted Gran, covering her ears.
"We'd better find it quick.
Look in the drawers!"

So they pulled everything out of the drawers.
No luck.
They found one of Posy's lost dollies ...
but no teddy.

"Waaaa!" wailed Baby Pig.

"Try the toybox!" shouted Pip.

So they tipped
out the toybox.
No luck.
They found Gran's
old hat ...
but no teddy.

"Waaaaaa!" howled Baby Pig.

"Try the kitchen
cupboards!" shouted Posy.

So they rummaged
through the cupboards.
No luck.
They found one of
Pip's old trains ...
but no teddy.

"Waaaaaaaa!" screamed Baby Pig.

"Try behind
the sofa!"
shouted Posy.

So they crawled behind the sofa.
No luck.
They found Mum's trumpet ...
but no teddy.

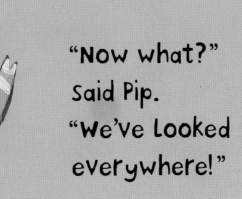

"**WAAAAAAAAA!**" hollered Baby Pig.

"Now what?"
Said Pip.
"We've looked
everywhere!"

Just then, Daddy Pig came in with the shopping.
"What a racket!" he said. "What's happened?"

"Baby Pig's lost his teddy,"
said Pip, "and we can't
find it anywhere!"

"There, there," said Dad. "Never mind."
He picked up Baby Pig . . .

and there was
his teddy!

"Look!" cried Posy. "He's been sitting on it all along!"
"Well!" said Mum. "And look at all the mess we've made!
The place is a pigsty!"

"But that's the way we like it!" cried Posy,
Pip and Gran.
"Yes," said Dad. "Anyway, I wouldn't call it
messy. More ...

"HIGGLEDY-

Mummy Pig

Posy Pig

Granny Pig

Daddy Pig

Pip Pig

Baby Pig

3

Good evening

4

Goodnight

Words to Know

Hi!

See you soon

day

evening

night

My name is,...

Ask your friends or family to play this naming game with you. One person needs to be blindfolded and twirled round. They then have to 'find' someone and ask **What's your name?** The person answers **My name is...** and says **And you?** Take it in turns to be the 'finder'. You could all choose an English name!

5

What's your name?

My name is,...

Choose a Name!

Sam	James	Alice
Alex	Emma	Isabel
William	Charlotte	

How old are you?

You will need two dice for this game. One person throws them and the other asks **How old are you?** The dice thrower answers **I am… years old**, putting in the number the dice add up to. Take it in turns.

8

How old are you?

9

I am nine years old

10

Happy birthday!

Numbers! Numbers!

1	one		7	seven
2	two		8	eight
3	three		9	nine
4	four		10	ten
5	five		11	eleven
6	six		12	twelve

Look at the numbers on the inside front cover if you want to ask some older people their ages!

How are you?

Cut out a circle of paper or card. Draw a smiley face on one side and a sad one on the other. Ask a friend **How are you?** as you show them one of the faces. They have to try and give the right answer depending on if it is smiley or glum. Swap round so that you can practise too.

13

I'm not so well

Words to Know

Awful

Quite well

So-so

Very well

Thank you/thanks

9

Where is...?

Find all of the items in the **Words to Know** list and put them on a tray. Practise saying the English words for them. Now close your eyes while a friend takes one item off the tray. (Cover up the English words too.) You then have to ask **Where is...?** whatever the missing thing is! Your friend will either say **Here is the...** or **Try again!** Take it in turns to have a go at remembering.

16 Try again!

Words to Know

book	colour pencil	pen
pencil	glue	rubber
	paper	ruler

What is it?

Look at this outdoor scene and practise saying the English words.
Then ask some friends or your family to play a drawing game
with you. You each take it in turns to draw one of the named
items and ask **What is it?** Everyone else has to try and say what
it is from the drawing (and without looking at the English words).
They say **It's a....**

17

What
is it?

girl

bicycle

picnic

ball

bird

18

It's a...

backpack

bench

boy

Here's the family

Spot the family! Look at page 15. Which four people are members of the same family? Point them out and say **Here's the son** or **Here's the daughter**. Use other words from **Words to Know** with **Here's the** too. When you have found the whole family you can say **Here's the family**. Check your answers on page 32.

19
Here's the son

20
Here's the daughter

21
Here's the family

Here are the parents

You say **Here's the daughter** (singular) but **Here <u>are</u> the parents** (plural).

15

I like,...

Have a look at this picture and try to learn the English words for everything. Then choose four things you like and four you don't like. Practise saying if you like them or not by using the phrases **I like…** and **I don't like….** For example, **I like flowers** or **I don't like mosquitos**. Practise with a friend and take turns.

cats

sun

trees

spiders

ducks

pigs

dogs

17

Where do you live?

The children in the pictures are telling us where they live. Practise saying the phrases. Then cut out four pieces of paper to cover speech bubbles 25-8 and number them from 1 to 4. Ask a friend or adult to call out **one**, **two**, **three** or **four** and say **Where do you live?** You have to try and remember how to say where you live according to the scene next to the number.

24 Where do you live?

25 I live in a house

26 I live in an apartment

27

I live in town

28

I live in the country

I would like...

Have some fun with this English shopping game for two or more people. Look at the shopping list and practise the words. The first player says **I would like some apples, please** and then points at the next thing on the list, the strawberries, on the market stall. The next player has to add them to the phrase, saying **I would like some apples and some strawberries, please**. Each player adds another thing to the list and the winner is the first one to say the whole list correctly. Then you can shout **That's all, thanks.**

The Shopping List

some apples

some strawberries

some bananas

some grapes

some carrots

some potatoes

some tomatoes

some lettuce/salad

21

A glass of water, please

It's time to eat so have a go at asking for food and drink in English. You can ask a friend or adult to say **What would you like?** All you need to do is choose something tasty from the menu and add **please**. You might also like to say **I'm hungry** or **I'm thirsty**.

What do you want to do?

You need two or more people to play this acting game.
Read the phrases and then cover them up. One of you
asks **What do you want to do?** and acts out one of
the activities. The other player, or players, answer
I want to... whatever they think the activity is.
Take it in turns to be the actor.

36 What do you want to do?

37 I want to watch TV

38 I want to play football

39 I want to cycle

40 I want to go swimming

Words to Know
Do you want to...?
Yes, I'd like to
No thanks

What colour is it?

Here's a fun game to help you practise colours in English with your friends or family. You will need a die and some counters. When you land on a square all the other players shout **What colour is it?** You say **My favourite colour is red** or whatever colour you have landed on. If you get the answer wrong you miss a turn. Good luck!

41

What colour is it?

START

FINISH

42

What's your favourite colour?

Count in English as you move your counter.

43

My favourite colour is...

Colours

red	green	black	orange
blue	yellow	white	brown

Where are you going?

These children are all dressed for their holidays. See if you can match the right phrases to the children. Say **Where are you going?** and then choose the right answering phrase. Practise saying this out loud too. Check your answers on page 32.

44 Where are you going?

45 I'm going to the beach

46 I'm going to the country

47 I'm going to the mountains

48 I'm going to town

Words to Know

On holiday

Have a good journey!

I'm wearing...

It's time to get dressed – in English! Have a look at the first picture and say **I'm wearing small trousers.** Now look at the second picture and describe the difference in the trousers. Say **I'm wearing big trousers.** Carry on describing the differences between the clothes on page 31. You'll need to use the **Words to Know**. You can check the answers on page 32.

Big or Small
You say **small trousers** and **big trousers** (plural)
but <u>**a**</u> **small cap** and <u>**a**</u> **big cap** (singular).

Words to Know

trousers	a T-shirt	a skirt	small
a coat	a cap	a sweatshirt	big

31

Answers

Here are the answers to the activities on pages 2-3, 14-15, 28-9 and 30-1.

pages 2-3

4 Goodnight

2 Goodbye

1 Hello, good morning

3 Good evening

pages 14-15

Here's the mother/mum

Here's the grandfather

Here's the daughter/sister

Here's the son/brother

pages 28-9

47 I'm going to the mountains

45 I'm going to the beach

48 I'm going to town

46 I'm going to the country

pages 30-1

I'm wearing a big coat

I'm wearing a big T-shirt

I'm wearing a big skirt

I'm wearing a big sweatshirt

I'm wearing a big cap

I'm wearing a small coat

I'm wearing a small T-shirt

I'm wearing a small skirt

I'm wearing a small sweatshirt

I'm wearing a small cap

50 English Phrases

1 Hello, good morning
2 Goodbye
3 Good evening
4 Goodnight
5 What's your name?
6 My name is…
7 And you?
8 How old are you?
9 I am nine years old
10 Happy birthday!
11 How are you?
12 I'm fine, thanks
13 I'm not so well
14 Where is…?
15 Here is the…
16 Try again!
17 What is it?
18 It's a…
19 Here's the son
20 Here's the daughter
21 Here's the family
22 I like…
23 I don't like…
24 Where do you live?
25 I live in a house

26 I live in an apartment
27 I live in town
28 I live in the country
29 I would like…
30 Please
31 That's all, thanks
32 What would you like?
33 I'm hungry
34 I'm thirsty
35 A glass of water, please
36 What do you want to do?
37 I want to watch TV
38 I want to play football
39 I want to cycle
40 I want to go swimming
41 What colour is it?
42 What's your favourite colour?
43 My favourite colour is…
44 Where are you going?
45 I'm going to the beach
46 I'm going to the country
47 I'm going to the mountains
48 I'm going to town
49 I'm wearing small trousers
50 I'm wearing big trousers